Best Handwriting for ages 8-9

You can improve your handwriting...

... just by practising regularly.

We hope that you enjoy working through this book.

2

How to sit for handwriting.

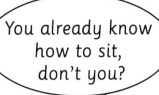

Of course you know how to sit,
but there are some important rules for handwriting:

✓ Sit comfortably at your table, so that you can see each letter as you write.
✓ Hold your paper still.
✓ Make sure that your table is tidy. You need plenty of space to work.
✓ Hold your pen or pencil like this:
if you are right-handed ...   and like this if you are left-handed.

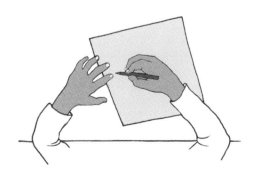

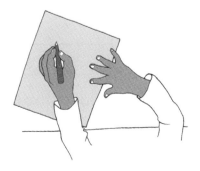

3

Just to get started...

...we're going to practise the alphabet.

Look very carefully at the instructions for each letter.

a a a a a a a

b b b b b b

c c c c c

a b c a b c

d d d d d d d

e e e e e e e e

f f g g g

d e f d e f d e f

Notice how the letter *f* goes through the bottom line.

4

Letter g goes through the line and is called a descender.

Letter h is a tall letter and is called an ascender.

Letter j is a descender.   Letter k and letter l are both ascenders.

m   n   o   p

m n o p
m̶ m̶ n o p
m n o p

m̶ m̶ m̶ m̶   n n n n n n   o o o o o o   p p p p p p

q   r   s

q q q q q q   r r r r r r   s s s s s s   q r s q r s

Which letters on this page are descenders?

Copy this sentence:

Letter p and letter q are descenders.

t u v w

t t t t t u u u u u v v v v v w w w w w

t u v w
t u v w
t u v w

Letter *t* is an ascender...

... but it's not a very tall one.

x y z

x x x x x y y y y y z z z z z x y z x y z

Now write out the whole alphabet correctly on lined paper.

a b c d e f g h i j k l m n o p q r s t u v w x y z

Time yourself. Use a watch or clock with a second hand and see how quickly you can write the alphabet. But remember - keep it tidy.

The letters that are not capitals are called lower case letters. On most letters the capital is bigger than the lower case letter.

Gg   Hh   Ii

Gg   Hh   Ii

Do your letters look as good as ours?

Or do they look better?

Jj   Kk   Ll

Jj   Kk   Ll

Practise the letter J again. Be very careful!

Jj Jj Jj

Mm *M M*

Nn *N N N*

Oo *O O*

Pp *P P*

Look how the lower case p goes through the line.
The lower case q does this as well.

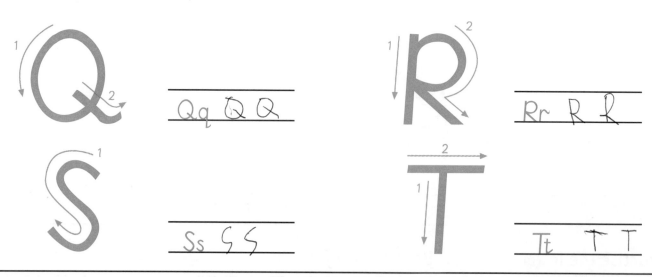

Qq *Q Q*

Rr *R R*

Ss *S S*

Tt *T T*

Mm Nn Oo Pp Qq Rr Ss Tt Mm Nn Oo Pp Qq Rr Ss Tt

Uu U U

Vv V V

Ww W

Uu Vv Ww
U V W

Xx X

Yy Y

Zz Z

Xx Yy Zz
X Y Z

Write the whole alphabet in capitals on lined paper as quickly as you can.

But keep it tidy.

Time yourself.

A B C D E F G H I J K L M N O P Q R S T U V W X Y Z

Are all your letters the same size?
Are they all sitting neatly on the line?

11

On this page we are going to practise slope joins.

slope join

slope join   slope join   slope join

an   en   in

Write the whole word.

Then go back and dot the i.

in ──────────────→ in

an en in an en in

co   do   hi

co co   do do   hi hi

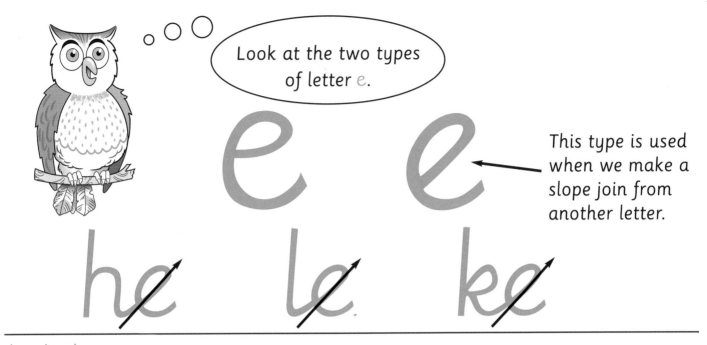

Look at the two types of letter e.

This type is used when we make a slope join from another letter.

he le ke

Look at this word: mine

Write it like this: mine

Then go back to dot the letter i.

mine

Do the dot last of all.

mine line dine

dinner

Look at all the slope joins.

dinner dinner

13

On this page we are going to practise bridge joins.

bridge join

on

ri   vo   wa

on ri vo wa

Look at bridge joins to letter e.

oe   re   ve   fe

oe re ve we fe

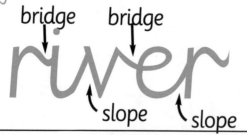

bridge   bridge

river

slope   slope

Don't forget to go back to dot the letter i

river   river

On this word we have to go back to dot the i and cross the t.

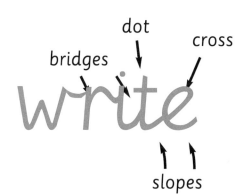

bridges   dot   cross

write

slopes

---

write   write

How many times can you write the word voice in one minute? Time yourself to find out.

---

voice   voice

How many did you write? Is each one neat?
Now try these words.

on   write   woman   fire

Look at these slope joins and ascenders.

Slope all the way to the top of the letter, then come back down.

al   eb   mb

al eb mb uh ck th

Try these words:

already already
lamb lamb
crumb crumb
comb comb
elbow elbow
thumb thumb
neck neck
shoulder shoulder

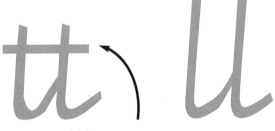

We need to be very careful with double letters.

We can cross both at once.

Try these words:

utter   utter

butter   butter

letter   letter

litter   litter

little   little

full   full

bull   bull

wall   wall

tall   tall

fill   fill

will   will

Look at these bridge joins to ascenders.

Copy these joins:

oh wh fl

ot rl

Try these words:

hob hob

where when why what

girl girl

curl curl

old old

fly fly

flood flood

Here are some more double letters.

oo   rr

Practise writing the words below.
Look at the spellings very carefully.
Make sure that the ascenders are tall.
Make sure that the descenders go through the line.

fool   fool
school   school
cool   cool
marriage   marriage
carriage   carriage

Now time yourself writing the word school as many times as you can in one minute.

Make sure that all the words are tidy.

We are now going to learn something new...

...joining from letter s.

S SO

Practise the join carefully when you try these.

sausage   sausage

sunny   sunny

practise   practise

practising   practising

Look:

practise

↑

This word is a verb.

practice

↑

This word is a noun.

When you join to an s you can make the top of the letter s a bit shorter.

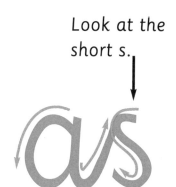

Look at how you can write double s:

Now try these words:

miss   miss

missing   missing

assist   assist

assisting   assisting

assistance   assistance

less   less

mess   mess

press   press

pressure   pressure

Here are some more new joins.

go yo jo

These are called loops.
The loops should not be too big.

Try writing go yo jo as many times as you can in one minute.

Keep them tidy!

Now spend a minute practising each word. Remember to keep your writing <u>tidy.</u>

go yo jo

gone
yellow
jam

What about loops at the end of words?

Some people think it's tidier to put loops where g or y come at the end of a word.

Look:

going going

↑ ↑
no loop loop

Practise these words:

playing
hanging
yesterday
staying

When you write a word that has a letter j in you need to finish the word, then go back to dot the j.

Practise these words:

adjust
adjusted
adjusting

Joins from letter b and letter p are very similar to each other.

Finish the first letter here, then go over part of it before sloping.

Practise the joins on these words.

pebble

bumping

problem

probably

Now for a speed test. Try each of the words below on paper for exactly one minute. How many can you write? Can you keep them tidy?

baps   public   possible   impossible

24

Joins from a letter q are always to a letter u.

Make sure that this is not a loop or your letter q will look like a letter g.

Practise the join ten times. Make sure that each one looks perfect.

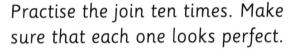

It is easy to use a slope join from letter z.

zi

Practise the join ten times.

zi   zi   zi

Now find ten words with qu in and ten different words with z in.
Can you think of one word with both in?

Here's something new.

You will need lots of practice.

We can write this letter x without taking the pencil off the paper.

Practise writing the letter x twelve times.

x   x   x

Practise a bridge join to letter x.
Write ox ten times.

ox   ox   ox

Now see how many times you can write box in one minute.

box   box   box

Look at these slope joins to letter x.

asc esc isc

usc

Try to flow from each letter to the letter x.

Practise each of these slope joins.
Write ten of each very carefully.

asc   asc   asc
esc   esc   esc
isc   isc   isc
usc   usc   usc

Write six six times.

Now try the word sixteen on lined paper.
Can you write this word sixteen times in one minute?

27

Now look at the new letter *f*.

Here is a slope join to letter *f*.

Here is a bridge join:

Practise each of these words:

if   if   if
fire   fire   fire
loft   loft   loft
left   left   left
feet   feet   feet
off   off   off
coffee   coffee   coffee
difficult   difficult   difficult

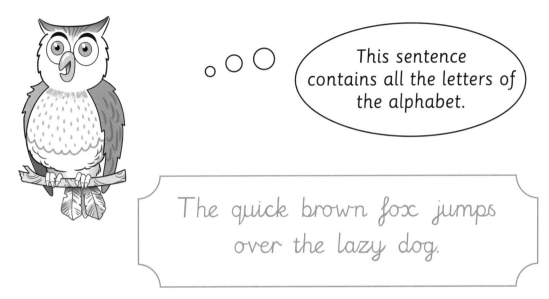

This sentence contains all the letters of the alphabet.

The quick brown fox jumps over the lazy dog.

Practise writing the sentence three times on lined paper.

The sentence below has only two letters of the alphabet missing. Copy the sentence carefully, then try to find which two letters are missing.

Yesterday, Eliza was sailing very quickly on the clear blue sea, just before six o'clock.

Try to make up your own sentence using as many different letters of the alphabet as possible. Use neat joined handwriting with all the sentences you try.

Punctuation marks are an important aspect of your handwriting.

Look carefully:

Full stops sit just above the line. Each one should be a dot not a blob.

Commas cross the line. Each one should be a small stroke not a tadpole!

Practise these sentences on paper. They include commas and full stops.

We wanted to go swimming, bowling or skating.
The autumn trees were red, yellow and orange.

Notice how the ascenders in the second sentence could crash into the descenders in the first sentence. When writing you sometimes have to space your words so that crashes don't happen.

Speech marks should be short strokes with a slight curve.

"Goodbye," said Jasdeep.

Look, the comma is written before the second set of speech marks.

Practise this short conversation:

"Goodbye," said Jasdeep.
"See you later," replied Neil.

Notice that we start a new line whenever a new person speaks.

Practise the words below on paper. Each one has an apostrophe because one or more letters have been missed out. Write each word five times.
Make sure that your apostrophes are in the right place.

don't   isn't   can't   they're   couldn't

Apostrophes are also used to show ownership.

Tom's house is very big.

Choose ten people in your class. Write an ownership sentence for each person.

Written questions always need a question mark.

Here are some questions for you to write on lined paper.
After each question leave two empty lines, then give your question sheet to a frien
Ask your friend to write the answers to the questions.

What is your name?

How old are you?

Where do you live?

What school do you go to?

Have you got any pets?   If you have, what are they?

Have you got any brothers and sisters?   If you have, describe them.